the Meteor Crater Story

by Dean Smith

PUBLISHED BY METEOR CRATER ENTERPRISES, INC.
Copyright © 1996

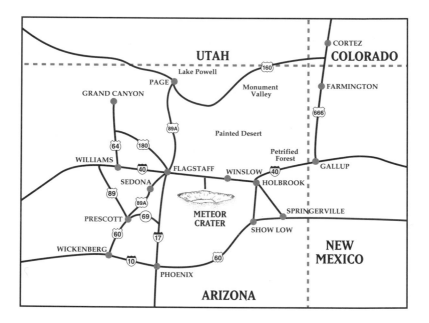

credits:
Design by Northland Graphics

Photograph on front cover by Peter Bloomer

Computer generated art on front cover by
Leonard Wikberg, Science Data

Meteor Crater from North Rim, showing the playa lake bed and white pulverized sandstone at main shaft.

FOREWORD

Fifty thousand years ago, a giant invader from outer space hurtled through our Earth's atmosphere at incredible velocity and collided with northern Arizona's rocky high plateau. The meteorite's explosive impact destroyed all living things within a radius of several miles, created the chasm we call Meteor Crater, and strewed rock and meteorite fragments across a wide area.

Should an object of similar size and velocity strike New York City or any other densely populated area today, it could kill some ten million people.

The world's best-preserved impact crater now attracts many thousands of visitors each year, drawn by curiosity, wonder, and a desire to learn more about the forces which created it. Some find in the crater a fascinating geology classroom, where rocks formed millions of years ago have been bared by the meteorite's impact.

Others want to see where America's Apollo astronauts trained for their historic voyages to the moon. Still others saw the three major movies made here and want to explore the site of those filmings.

To answer their questions . . . to explain how this awesome phenomenon was created . . . to trace the history of the crater and those who unlocked its secrets . . . and to ponder its global significance . . . for these reasons, this book has been written.

Has such a calamitous event occurred before on Earth, our moon, or the nearby planets? What were the results? Is such a disastrous collision likely to happen again?

We now know some of the answers.

—*Dean Smith*

CONTENTS

In an instant Meteor Crater was formed nearly 50,000 years ago.
(Illustrations by Leonard Wikberg, Science Data, Flagstaff, Arizona.)

CHAPTER ONE

Collision!

Modern man had not yet arrived on the untouched high plateau of northern Arizona on that fateful day some 50,000 years ago. Ground squirrels, lizards and other small animals scurried about the plain, searching as always for food to survive. Swirling winds kicked up dust devils and made the only sound to disturb the silence.

The landscape appeared very much as it does today: a broad expanse of nothingness extending eastward as far as the eye could see, and westward fifty miles to the majestic San Francisco Peaks, towering 12,633 feet into the cloudless sky. It was beyond imagination that this peaceful scene was about to be transformed into one of deafening explosion, blinding light and the unleashing of power so tremendous that it shook the earth for miles in every direction.

It started as a barely perceptible glimmer in the eastern sky, hardly distinguishable to the naked eye. But it grew in size and brilliance with each passing second, aflame from friction with the atmosphere, until at last it lit up the plain like a hundred suns.

And then, with a huge explosion, the invader from outer space crashed into the earth at an angle, exploding with a force greater than 20 million tons of TNT.

It was a meteorite, which scientists call the Canyon Diablo meteorite, weighing several hundred thousand tons, broken off from an asteroid in some celestial collision a half-billion years ago and cruising through space in all those eons since that time, until its path at last crossed that of our Earth.

Only seconds after impact, millions of tons of rock spewed upward, gouged from far below the surface of the earth, and then rained down in a deadly shower. A gigantic shock wave, which today would register on every seismograph around the globe, flashed out in every direction, destroying everything in its path. On all sides was a hellish devastation, where not even the shrill piping of a chipmunk was heard.

At last, the scene returned to near normal, except for the gaping wound on the Earth's surface. Where the fireball had ended its spectacular flight, a high rim now rose above a nearly circular crater more than 4,000 feet wide and 750 feet deep. That rim, still standing 150 feet above the surrounding plain, has survived 50,000 years of assaults by wind and rain. It was thrust upward from the interior of the crater by the impact, much as a fire cracker would leave an elevated rim if exploded in soft mud. The crater is not as deep today, 550 feet, as it was originally because it has been partially filled in by the accumulation of rock and soil over the centuries.

Although not quite so cavernous as it once was, Meteor Crater still astounds the visitor who looks down from its rim for the first time. The Washington Monument would fit comfortably into its depths.

Describing the fiery flight of this space monster requires all the superlatives one can muster:

▼ Although the meteorite probably was no more than 150 feet in diameter, it was zipping through our atmosphere at a speed approaching 40,000 miles per hour. At that velocity, it could travel from New York to Los Angeles in four minutes.

▼ The explosive force unleashed by its impact with the Earth is estimated at 20 million tons of TNT.

▼ One way to visualize the size of the resulting crater is to picture 20 football games being played simultaneously on the floor of the chasm as two million fans watch from vantage points on its sloping sides.

▼ On impact, the meteorite mostly disintegrated, leaving only small metallic bits beneath the floor of the crater. Many tons of remnants have been found, some as far as six miles from the center of the crater.

▼ ▼ ▼

Fortunately for those who want to see Arizona's Meteor Crater up close, it is only about five miles south of one of America's busiest freeways, Interstate 40, 35 miles east of Flagstaff and 20 miles west of Winslow. A paved road leads from the freeway to the crater. (One awe-struck tourist, upon seeing the short movie in the crater museum, is said to have exclaimed: "Wow! Lucky the damned thing didn't hit the freeway!")

Once the visitor has seen this natural wonder for the first time, a host of questions flood into his consciousness:

What manner of thing was this gigantic invader from space?

Of what material was it made?

What made the meteorite so bright?

When did it happen?

What did it do to the Earth's crust when the collision occurred?

Why did it choose that moment to end its spatial wanderings and plunge into our Earth's atmosphere?

Had such a cataclysm occurred on our planet before?

Is it likely to happen again — soon?

One answer at a time, each the product of intensive research by devoted scientists over the past nine decades:

What kind of object was this? Although the object itself remains the same, the scientific terminology changes. While in outer or deep space it is referred to as a *meteoroid.* If it should enter the Earth's atmosphere, then it becomes a meteor, or what laymen call a shooting star — a streak of light in the night sky. If it survives the fiery plunge through the atmosphere and impacts the Earth, it is called a *meteorite.* Untold billions of these objects have been zipping through space for several billion years after having been broken off from larger space travelers.

What was it made of? Meteorites are of three kinds: irons, stony, and stony irons. This one was more than 90 percent iron, with 7 percent nickel and the rest of trace minerals.

What made the meteorite so bright? Air in front of the falling meteorite became shock-compressed, highly incandescent and extremely hot. That in turn heated a thin outer layer of the iron body to incandescence and molten material streamed off during its swift passage. On impact, it disintegrated, melted, and partially vaporized. Meteorite fragments that separated early from the main mass during its fall continued to descend at lower velocities, landing on the crater and surrounding area. Thus they were not vaporized and some of them are now on display in the Meteor Crater museum. The largest, called the Holsinger meteorite, weighs 1,406 pounds.

When did it happen? The latest scientific data suggests that the impact occurred about 50,000 years ago.

What did it do to the Earth's crust when the collision occurred? Within a few seconds after impact, it created a huge bowl-shaped cavity. During the formation of the bowl, more than 175 million tons of limestone and sandstone were gouged out and abruptly ejected to form a blanket of debris surrounding the crater for a distance of more than a mile. Large blocks of limestone, the size of small houses, were heaved onto the rim, which was uplifted some 150 feet above the surrounding land. Seismic evidence indicates that the bedrock was fractured at least a half mile beneath the surface.

Why did it choose this moment to fall from space? These space travelers probably come from one of two sources: a belt of asteroids orbiting our sun between Jupiter and Mars, or from the tails of comets which periodically approach the Earth from beyond Pluto and then vanish into the unknown. Asteroids and comets have overlapping orbits and often collide with each other, sending fragments into orbits of their own. When these orbits cross that of the Earth, some of these fragments enter the Earth's atmosphere. One of these "Earth crossers," as such fragments are called, found its way to northern Arizona in this manner about 50,000 years ago.

Had such a cataclysm occurred on our planet before this event?

Geologists feel sure that, early in the Earth's development, our atmosphere did not affect meteoroids as it does today, and thus

Paintings by Don Davis showing the dramatic formation of Meteor Crater.

13

WHAT HAPPENED TO THE DINOSAURS?

Something catastrophic — a horror infinitely more terrible than any earthquake, tidal wave or volcanic eruption in recorded history — happened to the Earth some 65 million years ago.

Fossil records reveal that 70 percent of the living species on this globe disappeared at that time as a result of such an event. Dinosaurs and other giant reptiles roamed the land for millions of years before that time, but not long afterward. Great numbers of other animals and plants became extinct.

What happened?

University of California scientists Luis and Walter Alvarez and two associates are sure that a giant asteroid, some six miles in diameter, struck the Earth, producing a crater or craters many times that size. The impact site was in the Caribbean Sea, off the east coast of Mexico's Yucatan Peninsula, and the collision is known to science as the Chicxulub impact event.

A host of scientists now believe that the impact threw up enormous clouds of debris into the atmosphere, blocking sunlight for many months. The resulting stoppage of photosynthesis disrupted the food chains of all living things and caused the extinction of innumerable species.

Their proof lies in a layer of clay laid down all over the globe 65 million years ago, probably by the fallout from the asteroid's impact. This clay contains such noble metals as iridium and platinum, many times more abundantly than anyplace else on the Earth's crust, thus pointing to extraterrestrial origin.

Reinforcing the Alvarez theory is the recent discovery by divers of two giant craters on the floor of the Caribbean Sea. One is 90 miles in diameter and the other 120 miles across.

Dr. Edward Anders of the University of Chicago accepts the impact hypothesis, and his research indicates that the explosion set off flash fires all over the planet that added huge amounts of soot to the ejected debris.

Probably *that's* what happened to the dinosaurs.

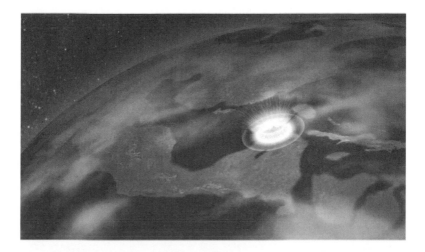

The Chicxulub Impact. (Illustrations by Leonard Wikberg, Science Data, Flagstaff, Arizona.)

the surface of our planet was at one time as pock-marked from falling bodies as is the moon. Evidence of those collisions vanished many millions of years ago in the upheavals of land and sea. But many space visitors have survived the descent through our atmosphere in ages past.

Scientists have now identified more than 150 sites of probable impact origin, of which Arizona's Meteor Crater is the youngest, best-preserved and the largest created in the past 50,000 years.

Is it likely to happen again — soon? More than 20,000 tons of meteoritic material now penetrate our atmosphere each year. Fortunately, most of it falls in particles no larger than grains of sand. But larger objects, from a few ounces to much heavier missiles, strike our planet annually. Meteorites as large as the one that blasted out Meteor Crater arrive much less frequently, no more often than every 50,000 years, on the average.

Really huge falls, such as the Yucatan Peninsula event, probably will not occur more often than each 65 million years. Or maybe longer — or maybe at any time. Nobody can predict with any degree of certainty. In recent years, scientists have begun searching the skies for Earth crossing comets and asteroids. They hope to locate and track any heavenly bodies that could pose a significant threat to Earth. It was through this endeavor that the Shoemaker-Levy 9 Comet was discovered months before it impacted Jupiter in July, 1994.

CHAPTER 2

Daniel Moreau Barringer:
He Just Wouldn't Quit

Native Americans roamed northern Arizona for many centuries and some of them undoubtedly explored the Meteor Crater area and picked up small metallic meteorites there. The first recorded mention of the crater was made in a report by an army scout in 1871, not many years after the white man's arrival in what is now Arizona. But the great hole seemed not markedly different from several nearby volcanic cones, so the pioneers thought little of it.

In 1886, an Hispanic shepherd named Mathias Armijo found a strangely formed iron fragment west of the crater near Canyon Diablo and thought it was silver. Specimens of his find were sent to chemistry professor G. A. Keating of the University of Pennsylvania, who analyzed them and reported they were about 92 percent iron, 7 percent nickel, and 1/2 percent cobalt, with trace elements including platinum and iridium.

Scientists still call meteorites from this fall "Canyon Diablo irons," because of the location of the first find. The name "Canyon Diablo" is from the village of that name located where the railroad crossed the canyon. This was the nearest post office and the only railroad stop for many miles.

Since that 1886 discovery, an estimated 15 tons of meteoritic material has been shipped away from Meteor Crater. The largest find, is in the crater museum. The second largest, weighing

Daniel Moreau Barringer.

1,050 pounds, is in the New York Museum of Natural History and the third largest, 1,000 pounds, is in Chicago's Field Museum.

The first scientist known to have visited the crater was Dr. A. E. Foote, a Philadelphia chemist and mineralogist, who in 1891 brought back more than a hundred iron meteorites and discovered within some of them tiny diamonds, formed under the tremendous pressures of their creation. Dr. Foote read a paper on these specimens before the American Association for the Advancement of Science, but for some reason never speculated on the origin of the crater near where they were found.

Dr. Foote's paper apparently motivated Dr. G. K. Gilbert, then chief geologist of the U.S. Geological Survey, to make the long trip west to examine the crater himself. Dr. Gilbert brought with him to Coon Butte, as the crater was then called, a team of trained investigators to determine whether it might have been blasted out by a meteorite.

Dr. Gilbert was one of the most respected geologists in the nation at that time, and few would dare dispute any finding he might make. However, he was not knowledgeable about the mechanics of impacts at cosmic speeds and thus declared that an object capable of digging such a hole would have to be as large as the hole itself. But where, he asked, was this gigantic object? There was nothing approaching that size in the area, and besides, his magnetic compass registered no deflections as he traversed the site. He also felt that a meteorite would have displaced more rocky material than was present at the site.

So, he reasoned, the crater could not have been of impact origin, but instead must have been made by a steam or gaseous blowout from below the surface of the earth.

Thus it was that Dr. Gilbert missed one of the great opportunities of his career. Not only did he pass up the chance to advance scientific knowledge by correctly identifying an important natural phenomenon, but his great prestige seriously impeded anyone else who sought to do so.

Almost a decade passed before S. F. Holsinger of the U.S. Forestry Service spoke of the crater and the iron meteorites found there to Daniel Moreau Barringer in 1902. A Philadelphia lawyer and mining engineer, Barringer was a man of keen intellect, considerable wealth, and hard-headed determination. He suspected at once that this crater must have resulted from a meteoritic impact, and theorized that a huge body of iron and nickel must still be buried not far below the crater floor.

If his theory proved to be correct, there was a fortune in minerals down there, waiting for some adventuresome entrepreneur to come and dig it up.

Holsinger Meteorite, 1406 lbs.

Having determined that the crater and the surrounding land was owned by the United States government, he applied for patents on two square miles of land — in effect a mining claim. The government granted his patents, giving him the equivalent of clear title to the crater in return for his promise to spend the time and money necessary to search for minerals there. The patents were signed by none other than President Theodore Roosevelt.

It was no great act of generosity on the part of the government, however. Records of federal agencies show that this land was deemed to be of no value, largely because of Dr. Gilbert's erroneous findings.

With a partner, Benjamin C. Tilghman, also of Philadelphia, Barringer formed the Standard Iron Company and the two set about to turn their dreams into solid cash. They lured Holsinger away from the Forestry Service and placed him in charge of the original exploration. Holsinger discovered the largest meteorite at the site, the 1,406-pound iron mentioned earlier, and it was named in his honor.

Crater interior showing main shaft house, lower camp and drilling rig for hole no. 24.

Because the crater was circular, the first fevered excavations were made in the center of the crater floor. But, to the chagrin of all concerned, nothing of value was found there. Low white mounds of pulverized Coconino sandstone can still be seen on the crater floor where that first disappointing effort was made. After that abortive venture, Barringer conducted some simple experiments and discovered that a rifle bullet fired into thick mud, even at a low angle, generally produces a round hole. That was an important clue. Could the meteorite have penetrated at an angle, and thus be buried off center?

In September, 1903, Holsinger dug shafts and trenches in the slopes of the upraised rim. When meteorites were found there beneath huge limestone boulders hurled from deep within the crater, Barringer and his team rejoiced in the knowledge that they at last had solid proof of the crater's impact origin.

Main shaft circa 1903.

When one looks at the southeastern crater wall, as Barringer did, it is obvious that the rock is uplifted there. Sandstone and limestone beds which were once deeply buried are now 250 feet above their pre-impact levels. That observation led Barringer to conclude that the mass had entered at an angle from the north and buried itself beneath the southeast rim. In high excitement, we can imagine, he invested more money in equipment and crews and watched the drilling progress with avid interest.

In 1904, a shaft struck water-saturated silica sand of a flour-like consistency and drilling was stopped by the resultant quicksand. Five holes were then drilled outward, encountering materials that, in Barringer's words, "dulled the drills immediately." In 1905, the company installed a steam-driven hoist and shafthouse. The resulting shaft disclosed rocks from all the different strata, scrambled together like rock flour as if they had been tossed into the air and fallen back. They also found a pumice-like rock which had been exploded like popcorn.

Barringer's discovery of undisturbed Supai sandstone a thousand feet beneath the surface convinced him that Gilbert's theory of a steam or gas blow-out from below could not be correct.

In a 1905 progress report to the Academy of Natural Science, he wrote "We can now prove that this crater is due to the collision with the earth of an extraterrestial body, possibly a small asteroid, which was presumably metallic in nature."

Mule driven winch used to lower equipment to crater floor.

Now there was no doubt in Barringer's mind of the crater's impact origin. But the scientific community remained unconvinced. He would spend the rest of his life and some $600,000 of his small fortune in trying to convince the skeptics.

Through 1909 the partners sank more shafts and drilled a total of 28 holes, probing 1,500 feet below the original ground level, but still there was no sign of the mammoth ball of iron which Barringer felt sure they would eventually find. It would be worth at least $500 million, he told prospective investors, but nobody was willing to risk money on his dream.

World War I ended and the decade of the 1920s began, still with Barringer and his increasingly discouraged team drilling new holes and pursuing new theories. His log records the difficulties: "six hours to drill two feet" . . . "last foot almost impossible to drill" . . . "the expert drillman says he has never encountered anything like this. We must be passing through streaks of solid metal."

Crew loading the Holsinger Meteorite.

In August, 1922 the drill bit became so securely lodged in the material that it could not be budged. All attempts to free the bit failed, and the final blow came when the cable broke.

It was the last straw. With the shaft down to the 1,376-foot level, Barringer called a halt and abandoned his 20-year effort.

But he would not give up hope. In 1928 he returned to sink a shaft south of the crater in hopes of avoiding water and quicksand. But they encountered the water table, and the operation required three days of pumping for each day of drilling. Sixty-three feet below the water table, with no indication of metallic presence to bolster his hopes, Barringer was forced once again to call a halt. His optimism had not run out, but his money was about gone.

Soon thereafter, the stock market crash ushered in the Depression and the last hopes of finding the treasure evaporated.

A few months after that, Barringer died at his home near Philadelphia.

One last feeble try was yet to be made. Geophysicist J. J. Jakosky conducted a study on the crater which led to the drilling of two more holes in the inner talus slope in the southwest quadrant. But 675 feet below the surface, the drillers encountered impenetrable masses and abandoned their efforts.

Main shaft house on crater floor. Main shaft reached a depth of 240 feet.

There would be no further attempts to find the treasure which many still believed must be down there, awaiting discovery.

Daniel Moreau Barringer had failed in his heroic quarter-century effort to find wealth beneath an Arizona crater. But he died knowing that he had accomplished a goal of much longer-lasting benefit: proving to a scoffing scientific world that he was right all along about a celestial body creating this giant hole.

In his honor, the name "Barringer Crater" is now used in scientific writings about this natural wonder.

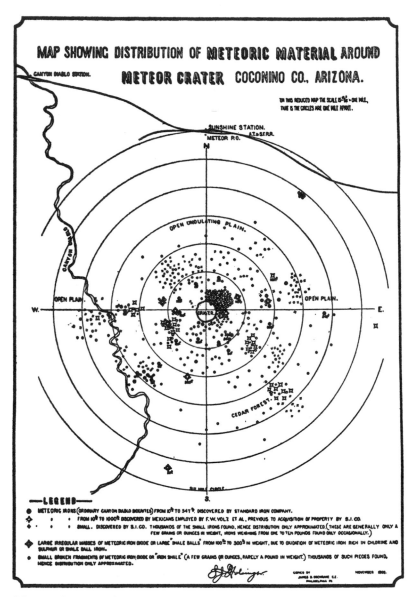

Meteor Crater and Surrounding area, showing distribution of meteorite material. D.M. Barringer, Report to Academy of Sciences, 1909.

CHAPTER THREE

A Rosetta Stone of Astrogeology

To geologists and meteoriticists, the June, 1960 announcement in *Science* was an exciting revelation: "First Natural Occurrence of Coesite," it was entitled. The article by Dr. Eugene Shoemaker in one of the world's most respected scientific journals told the story of his excavations of shocked rocks beneath the surface of the crater and his discovery, in those specimens, of coesite in its natural state.

Coesite, a high-pressure form of silica (SiO_2), had been earlier created artificially in laboratories by subjecting silica to a pressure of 20,000 atmospheres, more than 300,000 pounds per square inch. But it had never been found in natural state in the Earth until the discovery by Dr. Shoemaker and associates Edward Chao and Danial Milton.

In Shoemaker's paper he declared that:

"(1) Presence of coesite demonstrates that polymorphic transformation from quartz may occur under shocks generated by meteoritic impact . . .

"(2) Occurrence at Meteor Crater suggests that the presence of coesite may afford a new criterion for recognition of impact craters."

Coesite was formed in these rock specimens, not by pressures created in a laboratory, but by an impact force which staggers the imagination. Here, then, was an important scientific breakthrough.

27

Because of Shoemaker's discovery, geologists now have a powerful new tool for identifying craters caused by meteorite falls — one that a century ago would have kept Dr. Gilbert from making his erroneous declaration that Meteor Crater was blasted by steam from below.

Laboratory technicians at the U.S. Geological Survey continued their research on the specimens excavated from the crater by Dr. Shoemaker. They put them through exhaustive laboratory tests and in January, 1962 the *Journal of Geophysical Research* published a paper by E. C. T. Chao and others entitled "Stishovite, SiO_2, a Very High Pressure New Mineral from Meteor Crater, Arizona."

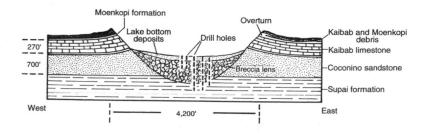

Cross section of Meteor Crater. (Illustration by Dorothy Sigler Norton from "Rocks From Space" by O. Richard Norton.

The article told of the discovery of stishovite in Dr. Shoemaker's specimens. Until then, this mineral had been made only in laboratories under pressures of nearly two million pounds per square inch.

Two million pounds. What incredible force did this giant space traveler generate in its collision with our planet!

Quartz has a specific gravity of 2.65. Tests showed that, while coesite had a specific gravity of 2.93, stishovite's specific gravity measured 4.28. It was thus more than half again as dense as coesite, a fact which was understandable in light of the much higher pressure necessary for its creation.

Now geologists have two recently-discovered criteria — the presence of coesite and stishovite — for identifying impact craters all over the world.

▼ ▼ ▼

These and other research discoveries here have led some geologists to call Meteor Crater "the Rosetta stone of astrogeology." Like the famed stone of Egypt which unlocked the mysteries of ancient picture writings, the crater has helped scientists around the globe to solve meteoritic mysteries that confounded them for decades. Now that early theories about Meteor Crater have been confirmed as facts, specimens recovered inside and around the chasm are compared with those in other falls to strengthen the new science known as astrogeology.

In recent years work has been completed at Meteor Crater in the fields of terrestrial impact craters, cratering mechanics and planetary studies. Modern geological and geophysical exploration techniques have largely replaced the earlier method of digging shafts. New approaches include the use of seismic, gravity, magnetic and electrical field techniques. Cosmic ray spallation procedures have been used to make a more accurate determination of Meteor Crater's age. Few natural phenenomena have been so exhaustively studied, measured and analyzed.

▼ ▼ ▼

Geologists have had a special interest in Meteor Crater because, like the Grand Canyon, it provides an open textbook on the formation of geologic features.

Four ancient rock layers lie exposed within the crater. Because they are of different colors and textures, they are relatively easy to distinguish. Let us examine them, starting from the lowest (and therefore oldest) rock:

The Permian age Coconino sandstone, oldest of the four, is grayish-white and about 260 million years old. It is about 720 feet thick at this site, but only its upper extremity is exposed in the crater. Once this layer was part of a vast area of sand dunes, which became fine-grained rock of sugary texture.

Next comes the Toroweap formation, a Permian sandstone mixed with dolomite and distinctly yellowish. It is only about five feet thick and coarse-grained in texture. Geologists tell us that it was formed under shallow water, showing that an ocean crept into this region and buried the Coconino sandstone dunes, probably while they were still loose sand.

Above the Toroweap lies the Kaibab formation, cream-colored and Permian in age (250 million years). It is 200 feet thick and contains fossils of brachiopods and cephalopods, both denizens of an ancient sea.

At the top of this geologic heap is the reddish-brown Moenkopi sandstone, about 240 million years old and averaging about 30 feet in thickness. It was laid down in relatively shallow water, and ripple marks are plainly visible on some of its rocks.

Geologists have encountered a puzzle here: Between the top of the Kaibab and the bottom of the Moenkopi there was a period of some ten million years, of which there is no remaining record. What happened? They theorize that, either nothing was laid down during this long period, or whatever was deposited had eroded before the Moenkopi sandstone began to form.

The trail around the crater rim is about three miles long. Visitors are not permitted to hike the full length of the trail because the increasing volume of traffic was endangering the scientific integrity of the rim. But one may take the guided tour of the northwest quarter of the rim, which departs the museum hourly each day, weather permitting.

Visitors may see all the crater's geologic features quite plainly from the lookout sites outside the museum. Strategically placed telescopes and recorded explanations make crater viewing even more enjoyable.

To the casual visitor, this crater may seem to be simply a hole in the ground. But to the eye of the trained geologist or the rockhound hobbyist, it is a fascinating revelation of how our Earth's crust was formed.

A DWARF FOREST

In several areas around the rim of Meteor Crater, one may encounter juniper trees 18 to 30 inches in height.

"How old would you think those little trees are?" a guide may ask.

Most people guess they are seedlings, perhaps two or three years old.

"Well, then, you'll be surprised to know that many of them are at least *700* years old!" he replies. To verify their age, some dead trees have been cut down, revealing as many as 700 annual growth rings.

Wind-borne juniper seeds fall at the crater and take root in the thin, dry soil. The peculiar character of this soil, the scanty rainfall, and the driving winds combine to keep these remarkable trees dwarfed for life.

Dwarf forest on the south east side of the crater.

both photos by Bill & Colleen Swift

31

It is a story of ancient oceans lost in unfathomable antiquity — of creatures which lived and died during uncounted millenia before the dinosaurs roamed the land — and of landforms and climatic conditions which have undergone many radical changes over eons of time.

Rim Trail: Looking from Barringer Point back towards the Museum of Astrogeology.

CHAPTER FOUR

Harvey Nininger, Meteorite Detective

He was not a prominent scientist — not even a geologist or an astronomer — but Dr. Harvey Nininger made a name for himself that will long be remembered in the science of meteoritics.

Dr. Nininger was a biology professor at tiny McPherson College in Kansas when he came down with meteorite fever, a pernicious malady that has changed the lives of many and which was to win him fame in a field so alien from his chosen academic discipline.

The glamorous study of visitors from outer space so capitivated him that he became one of the most avid of all students of meteoritics. Eventually he gave up college teaching and devoted himself unswervingly to the quest for knowledge in his new field, and to becoming the Sherlock Holmes of meteorite discovery.

Dr. Nininger roamed the Midwestern countryside, seeking out anyone who had seen — or thought he had seen — a fiery bolide on its descent through the atmosphere. By correlating the estimates of direction from various informants, he would patiently narrow down the possible field of search and sometimes, although rarely, find his elusive treasure.

He invited himself to hundreds of church suppers, lodge meetings, service club programs — anywhere he could find an audience — and regale the rapt crowd with tales about meteorites. As part of his presentation, he would pass around samples of meteorites and ask if anyone had seen anything like them on his farm or in the back woods.

Usually Nininger labored in vain, but once in a long while a farmer would come forward and say he had turned up such an object with his plow. Because there are considerably fewer rocks in Midwest fields than in those of many other parts of America, the odds were much greater that such a find might well be a meteorite. He would go to the man's farm next day, examine the object, and perhaps take it with him for further examination.

Iron meteorites were easier to identify because of their appearance and unusual weight. Stony meteorites, he found, usually had a thin black crust. Such a crust would indicate that the stone had been heated to incandescence in falling through the atmosphere.

We can imagine that Nininger's disappointments outweighed his triumphs a thousand to one, but he never lost his fervor for meteoritic detective work. For half a century, he pursued meteorites with unflagging zeal and succeeded in assembling by far the largest private collection of meteorites in all the world: some 6,000 separate specimens gleaned from at least 690 meteorite falls.

He did not limit his collecting to the Midwest, but roamed America and several foreign countries, following up leads whenever they appeared.

Part of his collection is now in the Museum of Natural History in London; the rest is in the Center for Meteorite Studies at Arizona State University. Dr. Carleton Moore, director of the Arizona State University center, earned national recognition for his work with the collection. *Meteoritics,* the official journal of The Meteoritical Society, was for years published under Moore's supervision.

The most fruitful field for Nininger's collecting efforts was, as might well be imagined, Arizona's Meteor Crater. More about that in a moment.

▼ ▼ ▼

Unfortunately for the advancement of meteoritic science, Dr. Nininger was not around when a 280-pound meteorite plummeted to earth near the Alsatian town of Ensisheim in 1492. King Maximilian used the fall for his own political ends, decreeing that the stone from heaven be preserved as a sign of God's wrath toward his enemies. Nor was Nininger present when Christopher Columbus, in that same year, recorded his sighting of a fireball that fell into the ocean not far from his ship in the Atlantic.

Many other notable meteorite falls were recorded in succeeding centuries and in many parts of the world.

Tunguska: uprooted trees are plainly visable within a radius of 30 to 40 kilometers of suspected center.

But the first major event that was actually witnessed by large numbers of people in modern times occurred on June 30, 1908 when a blinding fireball exploded above the Tunguska River in Siberia. Its ear-splitting detonation was heard as far as 600 miles distant. It threw a group of nomads from their tents 25 miles away and knocked down trees in parallel rows for 20 miles in every direction from the eye of the explosion. Only minute fragments from the blast have been recovered, however. Because no sizable meteorites have been found, some scientists believe the Tunguska event was caused by the head of a comet.

By odd coincidence, Siberia was also the site of another major event, which occurred on the morning of February 12, 1947 in the Sikhote-Alin Mountains several hundred miles north of Vladivostock. This was a huge fall, totaling some 70 tons of material, 93.5% iron, 5.37% nickel and the rest in traces of several other elements. Its impact created at least 122 different craters and devastated the surrounding area. Luckily, the collision occurred in an uninhabited wilderness and no one was killed.

SO FAR, NO DEATHS

We will never know how many human beings were struck and killed by falling meteorites in the dim ages of history. But we are reasonably sure that — amazingly enough — not one person has died in modern times from being struck by a fragment from outer space.

The only recorded injury from this source in the United States came in 1954, when Mrs. Hewlett Hodges was struck by a meteorite in her home at Sylacauga, Alabama. The 8.5-pound stone crashed through her roof and struck her on the left hip, sending her to the hospital with a massive bruise.

At least two other incidents of near misses have occurred in the United States. Incredibly, both took place in the same small city of Wethersfield, Connecticut, the first in 1971 and the second in 1982. No injuries resulted from either fall.

Dr. Nininger was one of the many investigators who flocked to the Chihuahuan desert in northern Mexico in the wake of another spectacular fall on February 8, 1969. That meteorite, weighing an estimated four tons, fragmented into thousands of pieces, scattering specimens over an area of a hundred square miles. One of those fragments narrowly missed the post office at Pueblito de Allende, giving the Allende meteorite its name.

Allende was a stony meteorite, and therefore more susceptible to shattering than an iron such as the one which formed Arizona's Meteor Crater. Its composition has been under careful study ever since its arrival 25 years ago.

Which brings up a fascinating point: Contrary to what many meteoritics buffs may hope, no visitor from outer space has yet been found to contain any element not found on our Earth. Apparently, our galaxy — or at least that portion of it that we know about — is made of essentially the same stuff as this planet.

▼ ▼ ▼

Harvey Nininger's name will always be intimately woven into the history of Meteor Crater. During the 1930s, he made a deal with the Barringer family which permitted him to collect meteorites from the desert surrounding the crater. In return he promised to turn over half of his finds to the Barringers. Although the family always suspected that Nininger kept more than his share of the meteorites he collected, the agreement did preserve many specimens which otherwise might have been lost to poachers. Many of them are now on display at the Meteor Crater museum.

During the 1930s, Dr. Nininger leased a small building on Route 66 (now I-40) near the road to the crater and put on display some of his meteorites.

He built a 25-foot tower there, from which one could barely see the crater rim, and charged visitors 25 cents to see what he called his "American Meteorite Museum" collection and to climb to the top of the wooden viewing tower.

(After January 2, 1942, when the Tremaine and Chilson families took over a spartan visitor facility in a decrepit stone building at the crater rim, Emma Chilson charged 25 cents to visit it and see the chasm up close. To those visitors brave enough to drive over the rough five-mile road to the rim, Nininger would say "go ahead," but gave the impression that the visit was included in his fee. Visitors' hard feelings over the double charge was the inevitable result.)

HAVE YOU SEEN A METEORITE?

If you think you have identified a meteorite, you should notify a university geology department or museum. Here are some common tests:

SIZE: The average person is most likely to find a meteorite measuring from two inches to two feet in width.

WEIGHT: Stony meteorites are about one and a half times heavier than ordinary rocks, and iron meteorites are three times heavier.

SHAPE: Most are irregular, and they are rarely round.

COLOR: The crust of a newly fallen meteorite is usually black. Weathering changes them to brown.

MAGNETISM: The great majority of meteorites exhibits some magnetic attraction. The irons are strongly attracted to a magnet and for most stony meteorites this attraction will be easily noted.

The best test is to grind off a small corner on a carborundum wheel. Iron meteorites will look like freshly-cut iron; stony meteorites will show silvery flecks in a compact stony mass.

Cross section of meteorite from Meteor Crater showing carbon deposits and changing patterns of different minerals caused by tremendous heat and pressure.

(above) The black crust and grainy interior of a stony meteorite.
(bottom) Iron meteorite. Polished and etched section and uncut specimen.

Dr. Nininger operated his tourist museum for some 15 years before moving on to other activities. He visited the crater often in later years, still searching the surrounding desert for meteorites even after his legal right to do so had expired.

We may assume that his many years of searching for meteorites in all kinds of climates and settings, in the healthful open air, contributed to his amazingly long life. He was still pursuing his fascination with meteoritics until his death, just beyond his 99th birthday, in 1985.

American Meteorite Museum.

CHAPTER FIVE

Enter the Tremaines and Chilsons

His colleagues on the governing board of General Electric Company had an affectionate name for Burton Gad Tremaine: "Lucky B.G." Lucky or not, this doughty Cleveland entrepreneur had enjoyed financial success in many business ventures, including insurance, real estate, auto manufacturing, and the production of incandescent lamps.

And in 1930, quite by chance, he got into cattle ranching in Arizona. Earlier, he had acquired an alfalfa mill and feed yard near Mesa, Arizona, which served many of the ranchers of the area. When the Depression struck, several of them went broke. Tremaine took what payment he could from his stricken customers, including a ranch in the Tonto Basin known as the Bar-T-Bar. To manage his new acquisition, and to be a partner in the enterprise, he chose Napoleon (Boss) Chilson, a former owner of the Bar-T-Bar and a man who had been a respected Arizona rancher for some four decades.

Chilson and his son Ernest did a marvelous job with the ranch, upgrading facilities and livestock, and acquiring large acreages of additional land. The Bar-T-Bar grew and prospered. B.G.'s son Burton Jr. also took a hand in the management, cementing the Tremaine-Chilson partnership that continues to this day.

In 1939 the Bar-T-Bar made one of its biggest acquisitions, buying the 100,000-acre Pitchfork Ranch from the Babbitt Brothers Trading Company of Flagstaff. The Pitchfork adjoined the Bar-T-Bar on the north and extended up to Highway 66, today's Interstate 40, surrounding the two square miles of Meteor Crater land owned by the family of Daniel M. Barringer. The Barringers at that time were leasing that land to a man who pastured a few horses and cows on it. Some of his horses, it was rumored, suffered from equine sleeping sickness. Because they often strayed onto the Bar-T-Bar range, they created a serious threat to the Tremaine-Chilson livestock.

So Burton Tremaine Jr. went to the Barringers, acquired the lease and grazing rights to the crater land, and moved the man with the diseased horses off the premises.

"While we're at it," Burton Jr. reasoned, "we might as well get the rights to operate the Meteor Crater facilities, too." It was almost an afterthought, but his foresight more than a half century ago has spawned today's splendid complex of tourist amenities.

The lease with the Barringers was signed on December 8, 1941, the day after the Japanese attack on Pearl Harbor, and was later extended to 199 years. The Tremaines and Chilsons have been managing and improving the Meteor Crater complex ever since.

▼ ▼ ▼

With gasoline and tire rationing going into effect in early 1942, there was little tourist travel on Highway 66 until the end of World War II. Emma Chilson, Boss's wife, was the entire staff at Meteor Crater during those years.

After the war, Daniel Barringer's sons, Brandon, D. Moreau Jr. and J. Paul Barringer, renamed the owning corporation. The Standard Iron Company became the Barringer Crater Company and changed its emphasis from a mining operation to one of advancing the science of meteoritics. D. Moreau Jr., a geologist and financier, served as president until his death in 1962. J. Paul succeeded him and was president until 1992. Today Drew Barringer, son of D. Moreau Jr. is the president of that organization.

Daniel Barringer's sons made it clear that it was the policy of the owners to regard Meteor Crater as a public trust established in the memory of their father. They have always dedicated their

J. Paul Barringer,
Chairman, Barringer
Crater Company.

Drew M. Barringer,
President, Barringer
Crater Company.

*H. Alan Tremaine, Jr.,
Chairman, Meteor
Crater Enterprises.*

*George Gary
Shoemaker,
President, Meteor
Crater Enterprises.*

Natural landmark plaque, 1968.

efforts to the education of the public and the preservation of the crater as a scientific treasure. Further, they wanted the operation to be a monument to the efficiency of private enterprise in managing natural wonders.

Bar-T-Bar's management concurred heartily in those goals and established a separate corporation, Meteor Crater Enterprises, Inc., in 1955 to operate the crater facilities. Ernest Chilson was the first president of that corporation. Ever since that time, Barringer Crater Company and Meteor Crater Enterprises have worked together in harmony. Chilson became chairman of the board of Meteor Crater Enterprises in 1981 when George Gary Shoemaker took over the presidency. George was succeeded in 2001 by Bradley D. Andes. H. Alan Tremaine Jr. has been chairman of the board since 1993.

How effectively private management has been in advancing the cause of meteoritics, educating the public, building expensive new facilities, and caring for steadily increasing numbers of visitors is evident to all those who visit the crater.

In 1968 the U.S. Secretary of the Interior recognized those efforts by designating Meteor Crater as a "Natural Landmark," thus assuring that the crater will remain unaltered by any owners in the future who might put profits ahead of the public good.

▼ ▼ ▼

When tourist travel started picking up in the late 1940s, the directors hired a series of managers at the crater, none of whom performed up to expectations until George and Ivy Foster arrived in 1954. This couple put their hearts and souls into the enterprise, lived at the crater, rarely took vacations, and for the next 13 years gave yeoman service to Meteor Crater.

George Foster wrote a book entitled *Big Hole: Two People on the Rim of Meteor Crater* which told the story of facility development during those years. In it he related how the crater slowly became known all across America, and recalled some of the amusing and memorable incidents in which he and Ivy were involved.

He described in harrowing detail the devastating windstorm of 1960 that ripped the roof off the museum and strewed its contents over the desert for a half mile in every direction. He told of the battle to get the Coconino County Board of Supervisors to pave the road from the main highway to the crater site. That battle was finally won in 1957, sending attendance at the crater soaring.

Foster's highly entertaining book was never published, but his manuscript has been preserved in the archives of Meteor Crater.

▼ ▼ ▼

In the twilight years of his illustrious career, architect Frank Lloyd Wright accepted Burton Tremaine Jr.'s invitation to submit plans for a new and expanded museum, gift shop and apartment complex at the crater. He did so, but the Meteor Crater Enterprises board chose to hire rising young architect Philip C. Johnson for the project. Johnson's design, combining glass,

Meteor Crater facilities, circa 1975.

native stone and stainless steel, was enthusiastically approved. In it, Johnson succeeded in creating a welcome oasis in the high desert—one which blended admirably with the landscape and which offered breath-taking views of the crater.

Needless to say, the buildings were anchored so securely that winds up to 150 miles per hour would not prevail, and the devastation of 1960 would never recur.

Since Johnson's time, facilities for parking, viewing, picnicking, and relaxing have been steadily improved. Well over two million dollars was invested in new construction during the next two decades. One of the new additions was the recreational vehicle park, service station and store near the turnoff from Interstate 40. In 1994-95 major new improvements, including elevators from the parking lot to the museum entrance, were completed at a cost of nearly a million additional dollars. In 1999, the new 80-seat theater was opened, and in 2001 the museum was totally renovated. The remodel was designed and installed by Formations Inc., a world renowned consulting firm.

In 1979, Meteor Crater Enterprises, Inc. hired George Gary Shoemaker as general manager, bringing new management expertise and imaginative energy to the operation.

Among the innovations which have been added are video presentations explaining how the crater was created and attractive museum displays which inform visitors about the geology and history of the area. A professional staff, uniformed and dedicated to serving the needs of crater visitors, is on hand at all times. Absolute cleanliness of all facilities is a never broken rule.

The forlorn little stone building which the Tremaines and Chilsons acquired late in 1941 has, over the years, developed into a strikingly beautiful complex that attracts visitors from all over the globe.

The old rock house on the crater rim which was the first museum, and Emma Chilson was its first curator.

Meteor Crater facilities as they appear today.

Meteor Crater now attracts over 300,000 visitors each year. The summer months are the busiest, but even at peak times you may be assured of a parking space and probably no waiting in lines.

It is located 35 miles east of Flagstaff, just south of Interstate 40, and 20 miles west of Winslow. A paved, all-weather road takes you five miles from the freeway to the crater facilities, which are open to viewing every day of the year.

Hours: May l5-September 15, 6 a.m. to 6 p.m.
September 16-May 14, 8 a.m. to 5 p.m.
(HOURS ARE SUBJECT TO CHANGE)

An Admission Fee is charged.

Amenities on the crater rim include state of the art theater, Meteor Crater Museum, which offers video presentations, educational exhibits, and hands on displays; observation platform and telescope viewing points: gift shop, lapidary shop, and Subway® restaurant; the Astronaut Wall of Fame, which lists all American Astronauts and their Missions, Apollo space capsule located in the Astronaut Park, and elevators serving both able and handicapped visitors.

Nearby, under management of Meteor Crater Enterprises, is a large recreational vehicle facility with full hookups, private rest rooms with showers, laundry, minimarket, Subway®, service station, playground for children, and recreation room.

For further information on Meteor Crater, call (928) 289-5898 or 289-2362; for the RV park, (928) 289-4002.

Area map.

CHAPTER SIX

Astronauts and Movie Stars

The cold war was at its frostiest in 1956, with Russians and Americans competing frantically in every activity from science to the Olympic Games. The two superpowers pointed nuclear warheads at each other, poured billions of dollars and rubles into sophisticated war machines, and struggled to achieve some triumph that would put them clearly ahead in the race for world superiority.

It was at that moment in time that Russian scientists scored one of their most memorable successes: putting a satellite in orbit around the earth. As Sputnik I soared around the globe in full view of an astonished world, Russians cheered and crestfallen Americans redoubled their efforts to accelerate their own lagging space program.

Determined never again to fall behind their Russian rivals, American statesmen and scientists established the National Space and Aeronautics Administration (NASA), a vast and teeming organization embracing many sciences and technologies. The first group of astronauts consisted of Gordon Cooper, Wally Schirra, Alan Shepard, Deke Slayton, Gus Grissom, Scott Carpenter and John Glenn, chosen in April 1959. One of John Kennedy's first official declarations as president was the promise that Americans would be landed on the moon not later than 1970. To bring that promise to reality, the Apollo program was activated.

But again the Russians scored a coup, launching cosmonaut Yuri Gagarin into orbit around the earth three weeks before astronaut Shepard became the first American to enter space. It was not until February, 1962 that Glenn was rocketed into orbit around the Earth.

Circling our planet, however, was far from enough. NASA had its eyes fixed steadfastly on the pockmarked face of the moon, and stepped up the training of the Apollo astronauts to reach that seemingly impossible goal.

The astronauts had been chosen for exceptional abilities as aviators, but now it was realized that any who set foot on the moon would need more than a casual knowledge of geology — at least enough to distinguish one rock from another, one type of geological formation from another, and an impact crater from one caused by volcanic action. Clearly, a crash course in meteoritics must also be on the training agenda.

That's when Meteor Crater became very important to NASA in the training regimen of the Apollo astronauts.

Here was the Earth's freshest and best-preserved impact crater, waiting to serve as a textbook for those space pioneers who might soon be inspecting first-hand the craters so readily visible on the moon. Moreover, volcanic cinder cones such as Sunset Crater outside nearby Flagstaff were readily available for comparison. The proximity of Lowell Observatory and the Naval Observatory in Flagstaff, and the magnificent new Kitt Peak telescope installations near Tucson also made this area an ideal training site for the Apollo adventurers.

To head up the instructional program of this new school of astrogeology, NASA chose Dr. Eugene Shoemaker, who knew more about cratering mechanics than any other American scientist. The program was activated early in 1963, with space immortals Neil Armstrong, Frank Borman, Charles Conrad, James Lovell, Thomas Stafford, and James McDivitt among the first students.

Their presence at Meteor Crater, with their space suits and other exotic paraphernalia, focused unprecedented national attention on the ancient chasm. The Apollo astronauts clambered

Apollo astronauts in training at Meteor Crater under the direction of Dr. Eugene Shoemaker.

down into the crater, sat through exhausting lectures, handled meteorites and rocks, and became instant experts in the mysteries of meteoritics. When one of the trainees ripped his suit on a projecting rock in the crater, he angrily declared that such a tear on the moon would have let his oxygen escape and cause his death. As a result, space suit materials of greater strength were developed.

Finally came that magical moment in July, 1969 when Armstrong and Edwin (Buzz) Aldrin became the first humans to walk upon the face of the moon. President Kennedy's promise had been met, with some five months to spare.

Apollo test capsule, boiler plate 19.

One group of Apollo trainees followed another, with Dr. Dale Jackson succeeding Dr. Shoemaker as chief of instruction, and then with Dr. David Roddy heading later groups. The program at the crater continued until 1971.

The quality of their training in geology and meteoritics has been evidenced in the quality and variety of specimens — moon rocks — which they brought back from the lunar surface. That training not only helped assure the success of lunar explorations, but it brought Meteor Crater into the world's consciousness as nothing had ever done before.

To perpetuate the memory of the astronauts and their contribution, Meteor Crater Enterprises has established the Astronaut Hall of Fame in the museum, and placed an Apollo space module for public inspection beside the family picnic area, now known as Astronaut Park.

▼ ▼ ▼

Astronaut Park, dedicated May 6, 1986 in memory of the crews of Apollo 1 and Challenger.

It did not take Hollywood long to capitalize on America's surging interest in space exploration and meteoritics. Three feature films were shot, in part, at Meteor Crater during a period of 11 years: "Damnation Alley" (1974), "Meteor" (1979), and "Star Man" (1985).

"Damnation Alley" starred the well-known actor George Peppard in a well-crafted but low-budget production.

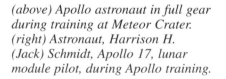

(above) Apollo astronaut in full gear during training at Meteor Crater. (right) Astronaut, Harrison H. (Jack) Schmidt, Apollo 17, lunar module pilot, during Apollo training.

"Meteor" was something else. It brought together a bevy of big Hollywood names: Sean Connery, Natalie Wood, Martin Landau, Brian Dennehy and others, and cost $18 million to produce. In its story line, a giant asteroid takes dead aim at Earth, threatening destruction of all life on our planet. Fragments breaking off from the plunging invader cause huge tidal waves and avalanches and cause widespread panic. So American and Russian leaders put aside their differences to meet the threat, firing a barrage of missiles that break up the asteroid and save the planet.

Two hundred movie critics and other VIPs converged on Meteor Crater to launch the publicity barrage for "Meteor," and the world premiere was held amid great fanfare at Flagstaff theaters.

"Star Man," starring Jeff Bridges and Karen Allen, told the story of an alien from outer space who was planning to be picked up at Meteor Crater by his space ship. Earth leaders who wanted to question him tried valiantly to prevent his departure with helicopter gunships. The filming brought unprecedented aerial combat action to the crater site and once again focused national attention on it. Later, "Star Man" became a popular and long-running television series.

Without doubt, the publicity surrounding the astronauts and film stars brought hundreds of thousands of visitors to Meteor Crater. They have been coming in increasing numbers ever since.

CHAPTER SEVEN

Meteorites Around the World

Techniques for impact crater identification which have been developed at Meteor Crater have enabled scientists to make positive identification of impact crater sites all over the globe.

It was Daniel Moreau's son, D. Moreau Jr., who proved in 1926 that two craters near Odessa, Texas were caused by falling meteorites. Later in that same year a field of 14 impact craters at Campo del Cielo, Argentina, were positively identified.

Since that time, others have been reported on an average of about one a year, except during the World War II years.

Another Barringer son, Richard, compiled a list of such craters and periodically updated it. His tenth updating, in a publication entitled "World's Meteorite Craters," was completed in 1971.

Also in 1971, Dr. Peter M. Millman published a discussion of these phenomena which included three tables. One listed identification criteria, another gave the continental locations of proven impacts, and the third provided exact latitude and longitude coordinates for the 62 sites on his list. According to Millman's compilation, North America has 32, Europe 10, Africa 8, Australia 7, Asia 3, and South America 2.

All these have been identified since Daniel Barringer declared Meteor Crater to be the first proven impact site in 1905. We can be reasonably sure that substantial numbers remain to be discovered. North America has the most, simply because interest in meteoritics has been much greater here than elsewhere. It seems certain that the vast expanses of Asia and Africa, for example, will eventually yield many more.

And, of course, with 70 percent of our planet under oceans and large additional areas under ice or otherwise inaccessible, it is highly probable that an even larger number of impact sites are down there somewhere and never will be discovered.

▼ ▼ ▼

Hoba West Iron of Africa.

Relatively few meteorite falls make craters. In fact, the largest meteorite yet discovered on this planet — the Hoba West Iron of Africa — made hardly a dent in the Earth's surface. Hoba still lies where it fell about 80,000 years ago, near today's town of Grootfontein, Namibia. Discovered in 1920, it is dark in color and squarish in form, measuring about 9 x 9 x 3 feet. But it is much heavier than it appears to be. Best estimates are that it weighs at least 65 tons.

Experts are not sure why Hoba did not make a huge hole on impact. Many speculate that it entered the Earth's atmosphere at a low angle, thus slowing its speed and making it skip rather than dig in when it hit.

Eskimos in Greenland found the Earth's second-largest meteorite, Ahnighito(Cape York), early in the 19th century and over the years cut off pieces of the huge iron for use in making weapons and tools. When explorer Robert Peary found it, his crew laboriously moved it — all 34 tons of it — a hundred yards to his ship and brought it to the United States. The Cape York meteorite rests today in the American Museum of Natural History in New York City.

Stony meteorites are usually much smaller than irons, but some whoppers have survived the fiery plunge through our atmosphere. The largest stony meteorite on record fell only recently — in 1976, in Jilin, China. It weighed about two tons, and the weight of other meteorite fragments which fell in the same shower totaled another two tons.

The largest meteorite yet found in the United States was discovered in the Willamette Valley of Oregon. The Willamette iron weighs about 15 3/4 tons, but probably was much larger when it arrived on Earth. Oxidation from the damp climate has greatly eroded it.

In comparison with these monsters, the specimens found in and around Meteor Crater are small. As mentioned earlier, the largest weighed only 1,406 pounds, .7 ton.

▼ ▼ ▼

Surprisingly, perhaps, the area which has yielded the greatest number of meteorites is Antarctica. Since 1969, when a Japanese expedition to the bottom of the world happened onto a number of meteorites imbedded in the snow and ice, other explorers have discovered well over 7,000 specimens there. Meteorites which have fallen over vast numbers of centuries are often pushed to the surface by the movement of ice in that south polar area. Because very small amounts of snow fall in Antarctica, these meteorites are relatively easy to discover in the blue ice.

▼ ▼ ▼

Dr. F.C. Leonard's "Catalog of Meteorites" listed and classified 1,563 falls as authenticated by 1956. The 1985 catalog of Meteorites by the curators of the British Museum of Natural History list 2,611 authenticated falls. Of these, 1,813 were stony, 73 were stony irons, and 725 were irons. Since that publication, another 270 falls and finds have been reported—18 were irons and the remainder were stony. Most of the meteorites recovered from observed falls have been stones, yet all the largest specimens found on the surface have been irons.

Why this seeming anomaly? It is because iron meteorites have a composition that is almost indestructable, unlike stony meteorites, which are more likely to burn up in the atmosphere during their descent, and which often shatter upon contact with the Earth.

Every new meteorite discovery provides valuable material for scientific investigation and further advances the study of meteoritics. For this reason, it is important that all persons with an interest in this fascinating science should report any suspected specimen as soon as it is found.

THE METEORITICAL SOCIETY

The Meteoritical Society was founded in 1933 by a small group of scientists who were interested in the astrophysical science which had become known as meteoritics. Again the Barringer name surfaces: D. Moreau Barringer Jr. was one of the founders and later its President and a major financial contributor to the fledgling society.

Dr. F.C. Leonard, who delivered the opening address at the Meteoritical Society's founding meeting, predicted then that meteoritics would one day enjoy "a definite and creditable standing among the sciences."

His prediction has come true. The advent of the Russian Sputnik satellite and the ensuing race to space created intense new interest in meteoritics. Membership has climbed well beyond the 600 mark, representing more than 30 nations. Included are geologists, astronomers and other scientists, as well as serious laymen who at some point in their lives have marveled at the sight of a fireball streaking across the sky. Members from many nations now attend the annual meetings, held at prestigious universities and other learning centers in both North America and Europe.

Dr. Harvey Nininger was one of the most enthusiastic of the early members. So was Oscar Monnig of Texas who, like Nininger, inspired hundreds of others to become interested in meteoritics and to join in the search for fallen meteorites.

The society's official journal, *Meteoritics and Planetary Science*, now enjoys a wide audience among both professionals and lay persons.

CHAPTER EIGHT

Could It Happen Again?

None of us spends a lot of time worrying about the possibility of being struck by a lightning bolt or meeting death by earthquake or tidal wave. Yet these natural calamities claim lives every year.

The odds against being struck by a falling meteorite are even greater. Despite the fact that 50 tons of space junk comes careening down to Earth *every day,* no one in recorded history has ever been killed by it.

That does not mean, of course, that no one will ever suffer such a spectacular death.

Miraculously, it would seem, virtually all of the major falls of recent history have occurred in sparsely-populated regions of the world. Had the two Siberian events of this century rained down their destruction on Moscow or Tokyo, the death toll could have been counted in the millions. Similarly, if a meteorite the size of Canyon Diablo, which blasted out Meteor Crater, were to strike Boston, New York or Philadelphia, the results would be catastrophic.

True, it is not likely to happen. Neither is winning a multi-state lottery. But someone wins a $50 to $100 million jackpot every few weeks.

▼ ▼ ▼

As noted earlier, scientists estimate that meteorites of Canyon Diablo's size will make their way through the atmospheric gauntlet and crash into the Earth approximately once in every 50,000 years. Even if such a monster should arrive, flaming but virtually intact, there is a 70 percent chance that it would land in an ocean or other body of water. It might produce a killer tidal wave, of course, but probably not.

Even if the meteorite landed on solid ground, the thickly-populated areas of our planet make up only a small fraction of the total expanse of land. With luck, it would choose Siberia again, or the Sahara Desert, or one of the favorite landing spots of past meteoritic history — Antarctica.

But then again . . . Who knows?

▼ ▼ ▼

The block-buster motion picture *Apollo 13* made it clear that objects entering our atmosphere — in that case, the Apollo 13 lunar module — must descend on a carefully calculated path if they are to reach the Earth's surface. Any other trajectory will make the object skip off the atmosphere, much like a flat stone skipping off the surface of a pond.

People in the North American West got a graphic demonstration of that scientific fact in August, 1972. A meteorite estimated at a thousand tons in weight — 15 times the mass of the largest specimen ever found on Earth — entered this planet's atmosphere and headed toward us. By good fortune, it entered on an oblique angle and bounced on by, leaving a fiery trail which even on that sunny day was visible to viewers from southern Canada to Utah. Had it reached the Earth's surface, it would have caused an explosion as powerful as that of an atomic bomb blast.

▼ ▼ ▼

Astronomers are sure that our Earth once was bombarded by flying objects and pockmarked with craters much like those on the moon. Hundreds of millions of years ago, however, our atmosphere took form and set up a protective shield against all but the largest of space invaders.

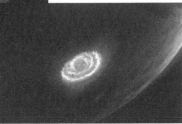

*Illustration of Fragment G
of the Shoemaker/Levy 9
Comet as it impacts Jupiter,
creating a transient hole
in the Jovian atmosphere
larger than earth.
(Illustrations by Leonard
Wikberg, Science Data,
Flagstaff, Arizona.)*

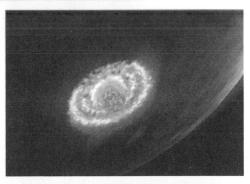

Even so, we have examples of global catastrophe that have been caused by such falls. The Vredefort impact structure of South Africa, which was created some 500 million years ago, was caused by a meteorite with a diameter estimated at 60 miles.

Much more recently, 65 million years ago, many scientists (as described earlier) believe a meteorite almost six miles in diameter struck the Yucatan Peninsula and caused devastation that led to the extinction of untold numbers of the Earth's animal and plant species.

Dr. Eugene Shoemaker estimates that a meteorite of such vast size will strike the earth once in every 65 million to 100 million years. If he is right, we may be about due for such a visit.

Shoemaker and his wife Carolyn, an astronomer, are among the most knowledgable scientists in the world when it comes to catastrophic space collisions. With colleague David Levy, they discovered a comet known as Shoemaker-Levy 9. Beginning July 16, 1994, more than 20 comet fragments impacted the planet Jupiter.

NASA's Hubble space telescope, in orbit around the Earth, tracked the comet fragments as they zeroed in on Jupiter, giving the world's astronomical community advance warning that a cosmic collision of mammoth proportions was about to take place. The news media quickly caught the excitement, and brought the story to many millions of people around the world.

Even those most knowledgable about what was about to take place were astounded when the largest comet fragment exploded in the dense atmosphere of Jupiter. A black hole, *the size of our Earth,* appeared above the face of the giant planet after the impact. It is estimated that the total explosive force was at least as large as the Chicxulub impact and equivlent to more than 100 trillion tons of TNT. Had the Shoemaker-Levy 9, or any object of comparable size and velocity, struck the Earth instead of Jupiter, it probably would have destroyed all life here.

The thought of such a collision on this globe, remote though the possibility may be, is a sobering one.

▼ ▼ ▼

The maturing science of meteoritics is one which fascinates growing numbers of people all over the world. When one gains an understanding of cosmic visitors — what they're made of, where they have been, how they got here, and what effect their arrival may have on our planet — a visit to Meteor Crater becomes infinitely more meaningful.

Meteorites will continue to blaze their way to the surface of the Earth, always in spectacular beauty and only rarely in destructive fashion. The story of these visitors from outer space, which Meteor Crater has helped scientists to unfold, is an ongoing one.

We may be very sure of one thing: The final chapter has not yet been written.

ABOUT THE AUTHOR

Dean Smith has been writing about noted Arizona families, including the Goldwaters and the Babbitts, for more than 30 years. A former newspaper reporter and columnist, he served Arizona State University as Director of Publications for more than 25 years before retiring in 1983 to research and write about Arizona's fascinating history. He has written 16 books and more than two hundred magazine articles. He and his wife Jean live in Tempe and Prescott, Arizona.

APPENDIX ONE

Known Terrestial Meteoritric Impact Sites

Ten Earliest Proven Impact Sites

Year Published	Name and Location	Lat.	Long.	Approximate Dia. (km)	Age(Ma)
1. 1905	Meteor Crater — Arizona USA	35° 02'N	111° 01'W	1.19	0.049±0.003
2. 1926	Odessa Crater — Texas USA	31° 45'N	102° 29'W	0.17	<0.05
3. 1926	Campo del Cielo — Argentina	27° 38'S	61° 42'W	0.05	<0.004
4. 1928	Kardla — Estonia	58° 59'N	22° 40'E	4.0	455
5. 1931	Bosumtwi — Ghana	6° 30'N	1° 25W	10.5	1.03+0.02
6. 1931	Henbury* — (N.Ter.)Australia	24° 35'S	133° 09'E	0.16	<0.005
7. 1932	Wabar* — Saudia Arabia	21° 30'N	50° 28'E	0.1	0.006±0.002
8. 1933	Haviland — Kansas, USA	37° 35'N	99° 10'W	0.02	<0.001
9. 1937	Boxhole — (N.Ter.) Australia	22° 37'S	135° 12'E	0.17	0.0300+0.0005
10. 1947	Wolf Creek — (W.A.) Australia	19° 10'S	127° 46'E	0.88	<0.3

Additional Proven Impact Sites (Since 1948)

	Acraman — (S.A.) Australia	32° 01'S	135° 27'E	90	<450
	Ames — Oklahoma, USA	36° 15'N	98° 12'W	16	470±30

73

Amquid — Algeria	19° 06'N	19° 15'E	0.45	<0.1
Aorounga — Chad, Africa	19° 06'N	19° 15'E	12.6	<0.004
Aouelloul — Mauritania	20° 15'N	12° 41'W	0.39	3.1±0.3
Araquainha Dome — Brazil	16° 47'S	52° 59'W	40	247±5.5
Avak, Alaska — USA	71° 15'N	156° 38'W	12	95
Azuara — Spain	41° 10'N	0° 55'W	30	<130
B.P. Structure — Libya	25° 19'N	24° 20'E	2.8	<120
Beaverhead, Montana — USA	44° 36'N	113° 00'W	60	>600
Beyenchime-Salaatin — Russia	71° 50'N	123° 30'E	8	<65
Bigach — Kazakhstan	48° 30'N	82° 00'E	7	6±3
Boltysh — Ukraine	48° 45'N	32° 10'E	24	88±3
Brent — Ontario, Canada	46° 05'N	78° 29'W	3.8	450±30
Carswell — Saskatchewan, Canada	58° 27'N	109° 30'W	39	115±10
Charlevoix — Quebec, Canada	47° 32'N	70° 18'W	54	357±15
Chesapeake Bay — Virgina, USA	37° 15'N	76° 05'W	85	35.5±0.6
Chicxulub — Yucatan, Mexico	21° 20'N	89° 30'W	170	64.98±0.05
Chiyli — Kazakhstan	49° 10'N	57° 51'E	5.5	46+7
Chukcha — Russia	75° 42'N	97° 48'E	6	<70
Clearwater East — Quebec, Canada	56° 05'N	74° 07'W	26	290±20
Clearwater West — Quebec, Canada	56° 13'N	74° 30'W	36	290±20
Connolly Basin — (W.A.) Australia	23° 32'S	124° 45'E	9	<60
Couture — Quebec, Canada	60° 08'N	75° 20'W	8	430±25
Crooked Creek — Missouri, USA	37° 50'N	91° 23'W	7	320±80
Dalgaranga — (W.A.) Australia	27° 43'S	117° 15'E	0.02	0.027

Decaturville — Missouri, USA	37° 54'N	92° 43'W	6	<300
Deep Bay — Saskatchewan, Canada	56° 24'N	102° 59'W	13	100±50
Dellen — Sweden	61° 55'N	16° 39'E	19	89±2.7
Des Plaines — Illinois, USA	42° 03'N	87° 52'W	8	<280
Dobele — Latvia	56° 35'N	23° 15'E	4.5	300±35
Eagle Butte — Alberta, Canada	49° 42'N	110° 30'W	10	<65
El'gygytgyn — Russia	67° 30'N	172° 00'E	18	3.5±0.5
Flynn Creek — Tennessee, USA	36° 17'N	85° 40'W	3.55	360±20
Gardnos — Norway	60° 39'N	9° 00'E	5	500±10
Glasford — Illinois, USA	40° 36'N	89° 47'W	4	<430
Glover Bluff — Wisconsin, USA	43° 58'N	89° 32'W	8	<500
Goat Paddock — (W.A.) Australia	18° 20'S	126° 40'E	5.1	<50
Gosses Bluff — (N.T.) Australia	23° 50'S	132° 19'E	22	142.5±0.5
Gow — Saskatchewan, Canada	56° 27'N	104° 29'W	5	<250
Granby — Sweden	58° 25'N	15° 56'E	3	470
Gusey — Russia	48° 21'N	40° 14'E	3.5	65±
Gweni-Fada — Chad, Africa	17° 25'N	21° 45'E	14	<345
Haughton — (NW.T.)Canada	75° 22'N	89° 41'W	24	23±1
Holleford — Ontario, Canada	44° 28'N	76° 38'W	2.35	550±100
Ile Rouleau — Quebec, Canada	50° 41'N	73° 53'W	4	<300
Ilumetsa — Estonia	57° 58'N	25° 25'E	0.08	<0.002
Ilyinets — Ukraine	49° 06'N	29° 12'E	4.5	395±5
Iso-Naakkima — Finland	62° 11'N	27° 09'E	3	>1000
Janisjarvi — Russia	61° 58'N	30° 55'E	14	698±22

Kaalijarvi — Estonia	58° 24'N	22° 40'E	0.11	0.004±0.001
Kalkkop — South Africa	32° 43'S	24° 34'E	0.64	<1.8
Kaluga — Russia	54° 30'N	36° 15'E	15	380±10
Kamensk — Russia	48° 20'N	40° 15'E	25	49±18
Kara — Russia	69° 12'N	65° 00'E	65	73±3
Kara-Kul — Tajikistan	39° 01'N	73° 27'E	52	5
Karla — Russia	54° 54'N	48° 00'E	12	10
Kelly West — (N.T.) Asustralia	19° 56'S	133° 57'E	10	>550
Kentland — Indiana, USA	40° 45'N	87° 24'W	13	<97
Kursk — Russia	51° 40'N	36° 00'E	5.5	250±80
La Moinerie — Quebec, Canada	57° 26'N	66° 37'W	8	400±50
Lappajarvi — Finland	63° 12'N	23° 42'E	23	77.3±0.4
Lawn Hill — Queensland, Australia	18° 40'S	138° 39'E	18	>515
Liverpool — (N.T.) Australia	12° 24'S	134° 03'E	1.6	150±70
Lockne — Sweden	63° 00'N	14° 48'E	7	>455
Logancha — Russia	65° 30'N	95° 50'E	20	25±20
Logoisk — Belarus	54° 12'N	27° 48'E	17	40±5
Lonar — India	19° 58'N	76° 31'E	1.83	0.052±0.006
Lumparn — Finland	60° 12'N	20° 06'E	9	-1000
Macha* — Russia	59° 23'N	118° 00'E	0.3	<0.007
Manicoouagan — Quebec, Canada	51° 23'N	68° 42'W	100	214±1
Manson — Iowa, USA	42° 35'N	94° 33'W	35	73.8±0.3
Marquez — Texas, USA	31° 17'N	96° 18'W	13	58±2
Middlesboro — Kentucky, USA	36° 37'N	83° 44'W	6	<300

Mien — Sweden	56° 25'N	14° 52'E	9	121±2.3
Mishina Gora — Russia	58° 40'N	28° 00'E	4	<360
Mistastin — Newfoundland	55° 53'N	63° 18'W	28	38±4
Mizarai — Lithuania	54° 01'N	24° 34'E	5	570±50
Montagnais — Nova Scotia	42° 53'N	64° 13'W	45	50.5±0.76
Monturaqui — Chile	23° 56'S	68° 17'W	0.46	<1
Morasko* — Poland	52° 29'N	16° 54'E	0.1	0.01
New Quebec — Quebec, Canada	61° 17'N	73° 40'W	3.44	1.4±0.1
Newporte — North Dakota, USA	48° 58'N	101° 58'W	3	<500
Nicholson — (N.T.) Canada	62° 40'N	102° 41'W	12.5	<400
Oasis — Libya	24° 35'N	24° 24'E	11.5	<120
Obolon — Ukraine	49° 30'N	32° 55'E	15	215±25
Ouarkziz — Algeria	29° 00'N	7° 33'W	3.5	<70
Piccaninny — (W.A.) Australia	17° 32'S	128° 25'E	7	<360
Pilot — (NW.T.) Canada	60° 17'N	111° 01'W	6	445±2
Popigai — Russia	71° 30'N	111° 00'E	100	35±5
Presqu'ile — Quebec, Canada	49° 43'N	74° 48'W	24	<500
Pretoria Saltpan — South Africa	25° 24'S	28° 05'E	1.13	0.220±0.052
Puchez-Katunki — Russia	57° 06'N	43° 35'E	80	175±3
Ragozinka — Russia	58° 18'N	62° 00'E	9	55±5
Red Wing — North Dakota, USA	47° 36'N	103° 33'W	9	200±25
Riachao Ring — Brazil	7° 43'S	46° 39'W	4.5	<200
Ries — Germany	48° 53'N	10° 37'E	24	15±1
Rio Cuarto* — Argentina	30° 52'S	64° 14'W	4.5	<0.1

Rocherchouart — France	45° 50'N	0° 56'E	23	186±8
Roter Kamm — Namibia	27° 46'S	16° 18'E	2.5	3.7±0.3
Rotmistrovka — Ukraine	49° 00'N	32° 00'E	2.7	140±20
Saaksjarvi — Finland	61° 24'N	22° 24'E	6	-560
Saint Martin — Manitoba, Canada	51° 47'N	98° 32'W	40	220±32
Serpent Mound — Ohio, USA	39° 02'N	83° 24'W	8	<320
Serra da Cangalha — Brazil	8° 05'S	46° 52'W	12	<300
Shunak — Kazakhstan	47° 12'N	72° 42'E	3.1	12±5
Sierra Madera — Texas, USA	30° 36'N	102° 55'W	13	<100
Sikhote Alin — Russia	46° 07'N	134° 40'E	0.03	0
Silian — Sweden	61° 02'N	14° 52'E	52	368±1.1
Slate Islands — Ontario, Canada	48° 40'N	87° 00'W	30	<350
Sobolev — Russia	46° 18'N	138° 52'E	0.05	<0.001
Soderfjarden — Finland	62° 54'N	21° 42'E	5.5	-600
Spider — (W.A.) Australia	16° 44'S	126° 05'E	13	>570
Steen River — Alberta, Canada	59° 30'N	117° 38'W	25	95±7
Steinheim — Germany	48° 02'N	10° 04'E	3.8	15±1
Strangways — (N.T.) Australia	15° 12'S	133° 35'E	25	<470
Sudbury — Ontario, Canada	46° 36'N	81° 11'W	250	1850±3
Suvasvesi N — Finland	62° 42'N	28° 00'E	4	<1000
Tabun-Khara-Obo — Mongolia	44° 06'N	109° 36'E	1.3	>1.8
Talemzane — Algeria	33° 19'N	4° 02'E	1.75	<3
Teague — (W.A.) Australia	25° 52'S	120° 53'E	30	1630±5
Tenoumer — Mauritania	22° 55'N	10° 24'W	1.9	2.5±0.5

Ternovka — Ukraine	48° 01'N	33° 05'E	15	350
Tin Bider — Algeria	27° 36'N	5° 07'E	6	<70
Tookoonooka — Queensland, Australia	27° 00'S	143° 00'E	55	128±5
Tvaren — Sweden	58° 46'N	17° 25'E	2	>455
Upheaval Dome — Utah, USA	38° 26'N	109° 54'W	10	<65
Ust-Kara — Russia	69° 18'N	65° 18'E	25	73±+3
Vargeao Dome — Brazil	26° 50'S	52° 07'W	12	<70
Veevers — (W.A.) Australia	22° 58'S	125° 22'E	0.08	<1
Vepriai — Lithuania	54° 01'N	24° 34'E	8	>160±30
Vredefort — South Africa	27° 00'S	27° 30'E	300	2006±9
Wanapitei — Ontario, Canada	46° 45'N	80° 45'W	7.5	37±2
Wells Creek — Tennessee, USA	36° 23'N	87° 40'W	12	200±100
West Hawk — Manitoba, Canada	49° 46'N	95° 11'W	2.44	100±50
Zapadnaya — Ukraine	49° 44'N	29° 00'E	4	115±10
Zeleny Gai — Ukraine	48° 42'N	32° 54'E	2.5	120±20
Zhamanshin — Kazakhstan	48° 22'N	60° 58'E	13.5	0.9±0.1

*Crater fields. Diameter given is of largest multiple structures.